LAURA'S POEMS

LAURA'S POEMS

Laura Ranger

GODWIT

'Sands' and 'The Sea' first appeared in *Stone Soup* (1991 and 1993); 'My Dog', 'Pete and Me' and 'Autumn Leaves' first appeared in the *School Journal* (1993); 'Omanu Beach' first appeared in *Journal of Young People's Writing* (1994).

Published by Godwit Publishing Ltd
P.O. Box 34-683, Birkenhead
Auckland, New Zealand

First Published 1995
Reprinted seven times 1995
Reprinted twice 1996

©1995 Laura Ranger

ISBN 0 908877 63 3

The publishers acknowledge the assistance of the Literature Programme of the Arts Council of New Zealand Toi Aotearoa.

Cover design: Christine Hansen
Cover photograph: Robert Cross
Typeset by TTS Jazz
Printed in New Zealand

CONTENTS

AGE 8

AGE 9

FOREWORD

I first heard about Laura Ranger's work from Brent Southgate. He edits the *School Journal*, had come across her poems somehow, and was going to publish some of them. I didn't quite believe the claims Brent was making for Laura's poems: a six year old? But then he showed me some.

In fact, there's no doubt about the quality of Laura's work. She's a real poet, and plenty of people think so. The first poem she wrote, 'Sands', was published in the American magazine *Stone Soup*; her second poem, 'Autumn Leaves', shared first prize in the Whitireia Poetry Competition with one by Lauris Edmond. And when I included her 'Two Word Poem' in *100 New Zealand Poems*, it quickly became for many readers the hit poem of the whole anthology.

> The toad sat on a red stool
> it was a toadstool.
>
> The rain tied a bow
> in the cloud's hair
> it was a rainbow.
>
> Which witch put sand
> in my sandwich?

I stood under the bridge,
then I understood.

I sat on the ledge and
thought about what I know.
It was knowledge.

The accomplishment there is quite extraordinary. We are given images, things to look at. Not only that, the way the poem moves along is well nigh perfect. There isn't a word out of place; there are deft and delicate hidden sound patterns (bridge/ledge/knowledge); and—above all—the stanzas are in exactly the right order, perfectly paced. Try rearranging things—swapping the first and last stanzas, for instance—and you begin to see how absolutely right the poem is, just as it stands.

'Two Word Poem' also takes its life from the pleasures of language itself. It manifestly enjoys words and plays with their possibilities—not to be smart or clever, but to arrive at a quiet point of wisdom which it even decides to name: knowledge. You feel, rightly or wrongly, that the poet has had a good time with a dictionary in the course of making the poem. Punning is sometimes said to be the lowest form of wit, but in some places, like poems, it can be the highest. This poem even ends with a pun it probably never had in mind: no ledge/knowledge. It honours the material it is made from, just as a pottery bowl or jug honours its clay along with its maker.

Laura Ranger plays with words elsewhere, even

coining her own, like unileaf, or nevergreen. She says of her poems, 'They are just ideas that came into my head'— which is a practical way of talking about inspiration. But you have to catch inspiration as it comes, and Laura has always kept a notebook, especially when travelling, so as to write down ideas and images when they do come into her head.

The difference between these poems and the work of some other poets is that, wherever the ideas and images initially come from, they are then worked on. Laura's first poems were written by hand—a pretty time-consuming and exhausting labour when you are only six. But by the time she was seven, she was using a word processor—typing on to the screen her initial phrases and thoughts, and then working on them. What seems effortless in Laura's poems has been worked at—and this must be partly responsible for the absence in her writing of those twin curses of children's poetry: clumsy rhymes and adjectival overload. Thus the crucial processes of revision, which reasonably enough bore and infuriate small children, along with quite a few large adults, were made possible, and even interesting, by computer technology. Changes could be made quickly on the screen, a text printed out, considered, then quickly changed again.

Poets have always liked bribes and needed patrons. The Poet Laureate does his job for an annual supply of sherry. The parental bribe that kept Laura Ranger encouraged was permission to stay up for an extra hour or so if she was working on a poem. It's possible to imagine the determined, sleepy poet at the word processor, images drifting into her mind and on to the shining screen. Maybe this is where the last verse of 'What I Would Take out of the World' comes from:

> I would take sleep
> out of the world.
> I would put rings
> around my eyes
> so they never close.

Like most poets, Laura likes her recent work best; at the moment 'Blue' is her favourite. But this book, as much as one by Jenny Bornholdt or Seamus Heaney, is filled with poems which talk to one another, even as they chart the changes in a life. The poem 'Disappear', for instance, is a progression from 'Pete and Me'. And subjects recur: there are poems about zoos and pets, parents and a little brother, the beach, Christmas, and—in particular—the seasons. And these are the poems, not of a pale, bookish child but of someone who is leading a normal, busy New Zealand life—climbing trees, going to the beach, riding a bicycle.

I think that these are wonderful poems, full of life and liveliness and intelligent, alert good humour. They set a standard for poetry by young writers—but also for anyone of any age who has begun writing poems, and is even now sitting up late, dreaming at the screen.

Bill Manhire

AGE 6

SANDS

My skin is as smooth
as polished wood.
When my mother strokes me
she sands me
with her hands.

My skin is as smooth
as a piece of driftwood
on Otaki beach.
Waves smashing,
and sand makes it smooth
as seagull feathers.

AUTUMN LEAVES

Red leaves
gold leaves
get as loose
as my front teeth
then they fall out.

In granny's garden
the tall oak tree
is as old as my mother.
It makes a red leaf carpet
on the ground.

Swish swish
I make a wish.
Lie on the magic carpet,
fly to the gold palace.
Swim in the
sea of leaves.
Swish swish swish
as quiet as a fish.

THOUGHTS

The Easter bunny
has curly hair,
pink ears, blue sox
and a grey sweater.
Do you know something funny
about the Easter bunny?
She really is my mum.

Father Christmas
has no beard.
He has a bald head.
He wears a tracksuit that is red.
He hides his sack of presents
under his bed,
and keeps his reindeer
in his shed.
I found out that Santa is my dad.

The tooth fairy
is a tiny boy
who wears a blue
elf suit.
He left four gold coins
in a jar.
That's neat.
I know the tooth fairy
is my little brother Pete.

GOD

The moon is a silver hubcap
up in the sky.
It is on God's unicycle.
He rides up high.

On the motorway in the black sky
the stars are streetlights
for God
to show him where to fly.

The planets are traffic lights.
Mars is a red stoplight.
At Saturn he has to wait.
When he gets to Jupiter
he has to go.

The clouds are God's thought balloons
sailing by.
He thinks about what we're doing.
He knows I am writing a poem now.

OUR PARK

In our park
I climb in a knobbly tree
and make a tree house.

I swing as high
as the sky.
I ride my bike
whenever I like.

In our park
we walk in the dark
as far as the buliben tree.

The possum grunts
and frightens Pete and me.

The moon is a silver balloon.
It shines brightly so we can see.

MY ZOO

I am lucky because I live
just across the road
from the zoo.
The animals are my friends.
I like watching what they do.

Varecia Variegata is really
a black and white lemur.
He comes from Madagascar.
He's a real screamer
when he calls to another lemur.

The otter swims
and does tumble turns.
Then he starts to squeal.
We say 'What's the matter, otter?'
He says 'Two dead fish please.
Oooh, that feels better.'

The American black bear
has black beary hair.
He's hardly ever there
because he's hiding in his lair.

The baby giraffe
gallops on his stilts.
The giraffe makes me laugh.
He has a very long neck.
He would need a very long scarf.

The New Zealand kiwi
lives in the dark house
and hides in the ferns.
He eats leaves and worms.
The kiwi can't fly.
I don't know why.

The emu is a very strange bird
because she can't fly either.
She lays dark green speckled eggs.
She's got extremely long legs
and walks on tip toe
as fast as she can go.

The spider monkey
has hands that are black.
She swings on ropes
and does her trapeze act.
She carries her baby on her back,
and eats celery for a healthy snack.

My favourite animal
is the mountain snow leopard.
He is endangered.
People make coats out of his fur.
That's a bad thing to do.
I'm glad that a few
snow leopards
are alive and safe in the zoo.

MY DAD

Sometimes my dad
is so grumpy,
that every time
he opens his mouth
a snap comes out.

Sometimes my dad
is angry enough
that he snarls
like a billy goat gruff.

My dad is as strong
as a wild lion.
He carries Pete and me
upstairs at the same time.
Sometimes he roars.

My dad is very very kind.
He often gives me a treat.
Like yummy chewy mint chocolate
and colourful lollies to eat.

My dad is
as fast as a cheetah,
as soft as a cat,
as friendly as a dog,
and as cuddly as a koala.

I love my dad heaps.

MY HOUSE

Rusty roof.
Paint peeling off
like an old wrinkled person.
Dad's up the ladder
painting new skin
on the house.

The fence is crippled and broken.
Mum's garden is a real mess
of rosemary and wallflowers,
and spiky purple pencils of lavender.

In our house
I muck about
in my secret hideout.
I can't tell where it is
because
it wouldn't be a secret
any more.

WHY DID ALL THE
DINOSAURS DIE OUT?

Tyrannosaurus Rex
was a meat eater.
He had tiny hands,
and scaly green skin.
His teeth were sharp
as a pin.

Tyrannosaurus Rex
was in a bad mood.
He ate all the other dinosaurs.
Then there was no more food.
So he died himself.

PETE AND ME

I love Pete
and Pete loves me.
Soon I'll be seven
and Pete will be three.

In our house
my mum and dad
let us skate up the hall.
Sometimes we fall.
I come scooting through
the kitchen door
and crash down on the wooden
    floor.

In the dark Pete says
there's a monster in the hall.
He imagines there is a dinosaur
in mum's work room.
We shoo it out with a broom.

Pete is cute.
Now he is learning to talk.
He calls my uncle's dog 'Dirty',
but her real name is Gertie.
Pete says
'frocodiles live in a trailer'
when he means
'crocodiles live in Australia'.

Pete is very funny.
He got into mischief in the shed.
He found Dad's best paintbrush,
and painted engine oil
all over his bed.

In my room
I play with Eloise.
We say to Pete
'Get out please'.
I hate Pete
when he wrecks our game.
He hates me the same.

WINTER

Everywhere the trees
are nevergreen.
The wind makes
my nose freeze.
The rain makes
a fast river
in our street.

There's a hole in the sky
where the rain falls out.
On the Desert Road
the storm
waterblasts our car.

At Whakapapa, the snow
is as white as a hospital room,
and as bright as the sun.
We slide down the mountain
on plastic bags.
Here we go.

SPRING

Fling off my winter clothes;
bring me spring.

Dad is mowing
the grass is growing
and I am blowing
dandelions.

Buds split open.
Blue irises
stand straight and stiff.
Yellow daisies
shiver in the breeze.
The cherry blossom
makes pink white snowfall.

I run up the hill
and cut the wind
with my kite.
On the trampoline
we get above the wind
and we fly.

TULIP SUNDAY

In the Botanical Gardens
bright tulips
spread out
like a yellow tablecloth
on a table with thousands of legs.

Some tulips
have red lips
and dark black eyes.
They bow and curtsy
in the wind.

AGE 7

BIRTHDAY

I look in the garden
to tell when my birthday
is near.
When the cherry blossom flowers
appear.
And pink green buds
of clematis
are bursting.

I listen in the kitchen
to tell when my birthday
is near.
I can hear
Mum and Dad whispering
about my new bike.

I can tell
when my birthday is here.
Dad is bringing
a heap of presents.
Mum is flinging
open my curtains
and singing
HAPPY BIRTHDAY
DEAR SEVEN YEAR OLD.

MY DOG

My dog Ali
is as gold
as a dollar coin.
He is as old
as a dinosaur.
He's half deaf.
All of his knees
are worn out.
He smells like
rotten cheese.

When we take Ali for a walk,
he rolls in mud puddles
and snorts like a horse.
He scavenges for food,
and finds fish and chips
with tomato sauce.
He eats the paper too
of course.

WEED SOUP

For magic powers,
mix together
four cherry blossom leaves
and nine pink flowers.
Wait for three hours.

Walk slowly in the flower beds.
Find seven white daisies
and two dried lavender heads.
Throw in one dandelion,
ten geranium petals,
and eight sprigs of mint.
Take five ferns plus
one handful of baby tears.
Add sand and water.
Stir for years and years.

Warning:
Children do not eat this soup.

NATHAN

Nathan at my school
thinks he is
extremely cool.
He dances the be-bop
in the class,
and plays the fool.

Mrs Herman
has hands on hips
and tight fish lips.
She turns
and looks stern.
She makes an announcement
'Nathan does not listen,
so he will not learn'.

MY SECRET SKATING RINK

Nobody goes there because
no one knows it's there.
It's hidden away in the trees.

Ruined old concrete
sprouting grass.
I skate fast,
whirling and twirling in a circle.

The wild Michaelmas
sprinkles the bank
and a blanket
of buttercups lies
shining in the sun.

The pine trees
stand straight and tall
like middle-aged men
covered with warts.
Then I hear the bellbird call
above the shivering grass.

WHERE DO BURGLARS LIVE?

Burglars might live in bushes
if they haven't been caught.
They would wear green
so they couldn't be seen.

They might creep
into people's sheds
with black balaclavas
over their heads.
Or hide under houses
and creep out at night
to steal jewellery
or start a fight.

Burglars murk about
in rusty cars
spying on people.
Sometimes they shout
and swear at the police.

When they've been caught
burglars live in jail.
They eat bread
that's gone stale.
After a while they get
lonely and turn pale.

SUMMER

There's snow in summer;
it's the white buds
on the pohutukawa trees.
Later they burst
into red flames.

In summer
I can't walk barefoot
in the clover
because of bees,
yellow and black
as day and night.
Bees buzzing and sizzling
like sausages
at a barbecue.

My summer fruits are
strawberries, peaches
and nectarines.
I eat lots and lots and lots,
until I come out in spots.

WINDREST

At Windrest cottage garden
the wind has a holiday
from blowing.
It rests in the summerhouse
while the sweet birds sing
and red roses clamber
up the fence.

I walk barefoot
in mud and grass
past the waterlilies
and flowerbeds.
Shhhhh the flowers
are sleeping
and the hydrangea
is night blue.

I find a small
treehouse
where sweetpeas
tiptoe up the wall.

The wind is homesick
and feeling faint.
She arrives home sighing
in the garden.
A dovecote sways
in the olive tree.

OMANU BEACH

To the people
in the fishing boat
out at sea
we are on the horizon.
They might see me
paddling on the shore
stabbing jellyfish
with a stick
in the heart.

At sunset
we were plodding
along the sand dunes.
The sun was spying on us
through a telescope,
from behind the trees.

NUMBER TWO DOG POEM

When the sun is behind him
his shadow is like an arrow.

His mouth is as black
as a burnt piece of coal.

His ears hang down
like golden autumn leaves.

The fur on his neck
is as frilly as a ballet tutu,

but his legs are like
worn out stockings.

His tail flaps in the wind
like a piece of flax.

OTAKI POEM

At Otaki we run like
wild horses on the beach
among the scattered shells
and mountains of tussock grass.
I dance over the
rough and tumble weed.
The waves sound like
breaking glass.
Take care.
The undertow might reach
out its hand and
grab you by the leg
and drag you under.

We hunt for wild animals.
The driftwood snake
has one wrinkled eye.
There are rough freckles
on the fish and
the crocodile has a fence
of spikes along its back.
We tame the wild
beach creatures
then I sprint home
up the track.

SPRING TIDE

The wind
is strong and wild,
and the spring tide
makes the beach disappear.
The clouds curl and turn
black and grey
like my mother's hair.

Seagulls cry and moan.
The wind whips
right through my skin,
and deep freezes me.
I grow as cold as stone.

MUM

Her hair curls
like fern fronds.

Her eyes are like
speckled green birds' eggs.

Her glasses are two pools
of clear water.

Her nose is blunt.

Her hands are wrinkled and kind.
She reaches out to touch me.

I love my mum
forty four million
times around the world.

THE SEA

the mist smudges out
Kapiti Island

the hills curve and rise
like loaves of bread

the sun sprinkles glitter
on the sea

the wind is writing
what it knows
in lines along the water

IN AUSTRALIA

In Australia I saw ten billion flies.
They stick on your back,
they crawl on your eyes.

At Pebbly Beach the rosellas
are a crimson streak of light.
They sit in your hair
and most of them bite.

While a family was swimming
some kangaroos kidnapped their lunch.
They undid the picnic basket
and soon they started to munch.

At Featherdale Wildlife Park
the wombats sleep in beds
that look like babies' cradles
inside little tin sheds.

In Goulburn there's a concrete sheep
with huge green eyes.
It is two storeys high.
I'm not telling you a lie.

At Batemans Bay we swam all day
and afterwards we stood and stared.
The sky and the hills were on fire
and the full moon was rising behind us.
As the sun dived lower,
the moon climbed higher.

TWO WORD POEM

The toad sat on a red stool
it was a toadstool.

The rain tied a bow
in the cloud's hair
it was a rainbow.

Which witch put sand
in my sandwich?

I stood under the bridge,
then I understood.

I sat on the ledge and
thought about what I know.
It was knowledge.

AUTUMN 2

the leaves are bleeding
before they fall
to the ground

they make no sound

AUTUMN GOLD

The money tree flings the leaves down
the dollars flutter to the ground

the notes are lying in deep heaps
they look as messy as my bedroom

I am climbing the bank
and rustling in the leaves

I go mining for gold.

THE TREE

The tree stretches up tall
and ties itself in a knot.
The tree has green hair
like a punk.
When you chop a tree down
tree blood pours out.
I can hear the tree crying.

UNILEAF

A unileaf tree
has only one leaf,
it is the last leaf
that falls.

It hangs
like an odd sock
flapping
on the washing line.

THE FROST

Silver Jack Frost
and glistening Jill Snow
go up the hill.
The colour is lost
the trees are still.

THE SEAGULL

One wuthering wet day in May
a giant black-backed gull
with a twisted left leg
waddled into our garden
from out of the grey.

We fed her and we stroked her
and we called her Sally
but she died the next day.

AGE 8

A DOG NAMED ZAK

He has springs
in his short legs.
He jumps like a yoyo
behind the gate.
Marion lets him out.
He shoots like a bullet
back and forth
across the street.
His brain is aching
with electricity
that is making him run.
He is a marathon streaker
dashing ten different
ways at once.

WHAT I WOULD TAKE
OUT OF THE WORLD

I would take lawnmowers
out of the world
so I can run
in the long grass
and lie down and hide.

I would take homework
out of the world
and criminals
especially murderers.

I would take sleep
out of the world.
I would put rings
around my eyes
so they never close.

THE WORLD

In our secret garden
the flowers welcome me
like birds nodding
their heads on stems.
The grass shivers
and tingles down its spine.

The clouds are clouding
in the morning,
so the flowers shut
like a door.
When it is sunny
in the afternoon
the flowers open
like a window.

Where does the sky
meet the earth?
Outside, everywhere,
in my back yard.

DISAPPEAR

Boys are annoying.
I am going to send
my little brother
to the furthest planet
away from earth.
My disappearing spell
is a gross mixture
of frog's blood and pearls
to give him warts.
I will send spies to
see if it has worked.
I have a secret word
but I cannot tell.
The hardest part
of the spell
is getting him
to drink it.

THE ALIEN

The spiky cabbage tree
looks like an alien from Mars
standing alone in a field
not knowing what to do
or how to speak the language.
The cows are just mooching
around in the paddock
eating grass.

IT GETS DARK

The crescent moon
is a slick snake
which has come too soon.
The sunset is fading
like my flowery sundress.
It is not dark yet.

Now a very old blanket
with starry holes in it
is covering the sky.
The sun on the other side
is begging to get through.

The trees are lurking.
It gets dark.

AGE 9

ANOTHER ZOO POEM

The Himalayan thar
has hair like a balaclava.
He is hiding up a tree
like an escaped prisoner.

The baboon's bottom
is a crimson moon.
He is exploring it
for fleas.

This is a smelly verse.
The stench of the piss
of the serval cat
gets worse and worse.

The gibbon flaps her arms
and flies through the air
like a bird.

KIP'S EAR PROBLEM

He stands outside the window
with his paws up on the sill.
His ears like sails in the wind.

He gallops across the field,
his ears soar up and down
like a seagull.

When he stands out in the rain
his ears are drenched lettuce leaves.

You can get Kip's ears
and cover his eyes with them
and play Blind Man's Buff.

At Christmas, Kip climbs up the chimney
and his ears turn black.
He is Santa's reindeer in disguise.

BLUE

My cat Blue is like
a flying white cloud
skimming across the sky.

At night Blue snuggles
down into my bed
but he's a toe thief.
He sleeps in his clothes
so he's the first one
dressed in the morning.

Blue is an opera singer.
He gets fatter and fatter
On Ocean Fish Platter.

For his birthday
I will give my cat
a Jellimeat birthday cake
and a party hat.